WORM FARMING

THE PRACTICAL GUIDE TO THIS UNIQUE FORM OF NATURAL COMPOSTING...

AARON "WORMS" JONES

A D

ISBN: 978-3-96772-001-3

The cover for this work was created with the help of an image from "Depositphotos".

The Icons used in this work were designed by Freepik from Flaticon

CONTENTS

FOREWORD

Hi, my name is Aaron "*Worms*" Jones and I'm a member of The Brothers Green.

We are a group of friends (read - "green thumbs") who love all things horticulture. Our purpose is to help others in all aspects of growing, pruning, composting... and well, just plain old gardening!

Out of our little group I am the expert in all things worm farming and composting.

You may have grabbed this book because you are interested in finding out more about the activity.

Perhaps you are looking for specific guidance on *designing* your own worm farm...

... Or you are simply an enthusiast with years of experience and you want some extra tips to further refine your skills.

Whatever the reason, **I want to thank you for reading and checking out this book.**

This book is dedicated entirely to teaching you all I know about worm farming. In it you will learn about everything from the benefits of vermicomposting to dealing with possible issues you may have with your worm farm. Read on for straight to the point information and plenty of tips and tricks.

Compost created by composting worms is called vermicompost, and refined compost material is called worm castings (or worm poop).

-Ed Hubbard-

INTRODUCTION

Worm Farming | Vermiculture (Vermicomposting) | Worm-composting

In simplest terms, these words describe the process of recycling organic matter with the help of earthworms.

> Now why would anyone be interested in any of this "*worm farming*"?

Well for one, there is a growing concern for our environment. As human populations have continued to grow, unfortunately, so has our mistreatment of the planet. We haven't been taking the best care of mother nature and have become accustomed to a lifestyle that isn't sustainable.

Luckily, more and more individuals are looking at ways they can make a difference. People have gotten better at reducing their waste footprint and recycling properly.

There is also a greater interest in worm farming. The practice is a great way to reduce pressure on landfills as worms are excellent at fertilizing the earth. It may be hard to believe, but some important worm populations are dwindling. Farmers use a lot of chemicals and pesticides to grow their crops. Earthworms cannot handle these chemicals and they are slowly dying out. What makes the situation even worse is the fact that earthworms naturally help grow the crops and plants.

Worm farming helps worms continue to thrive and also makes for a better planet. Besides these great benefits there are plenty more reasons to get involved with the hobby. Let's consider some more situations below...

Fun

The hobby is a lot of fun to take part in. It is not something that takes a full-time commitment and it is very relaxing. The costs associated with starting out are also quite low. For many it gets very addictive, and this leads to the next possibility...

Business

Some people start worm farming as just a hobby to keep them busy, but overtime it turns into a business opportunity. The fertilizer the worms produce naturally is highly sought after. It is rich in minerals and allows plants to flourish. Besides the healthy earth you can create and sell there is also interest in the worms themselves. In worm farming the population of worms can grow quite fast. In your farm there will be no predators helping control the population. Many start selling their excess worms to people who need fish bait...

Fishing

Worms have been used as fish bait for a long time. If you partake in a lot of fishing and need bait, it can be better for you to have a worm farm. It will be a lot cheaper in the long run and it is not very time intensive.

Worms are commonly seen as slimy and gooey creatures but they have a very important job. Nowadays, with more people getting involved with the environment, worm farming has highlighted their value.

A great feature of the hobby is that it doesn't require a lot of space. Worm farming is great if you have a large yard to work with, but it is possible to join the fun even if you have only a balcony or apartment to work with.

It is a simple way to create potting soil for plants in your own home. Leftover scraps from fruits and vegetables don't need to go to waste. They are perfect additions to your self-sustaining farm.

Charles Darwin studied worms for 38 years. He even published a book on them in 1881 with his findings, just before he died. In this book he suggested earthworms are the most important creatures on Earth.

-Wormfarmguru.com-

1

COMPOSTING

Composting and worm farming are activities that work hand in hand. We can all learn more about the environment in the process and save waste from being dumped into landfills. If you and your family have organic waste, composting can help recycle it. Worms in your farm will eat it and what they leave behind can be used as fertilizer.

This fertilizer will help your plants, fruits and vegetables grow larger. The fresh food you will be able to create is amazing.

Lets have a look at some of the things you will need to consider:

. . .

Moisture:

Compost piles should remain moist. This does not mean that it needs a lot of water. Too much moisture will mess up the compost pile.

Aeration:

Aeration is the process of 'turning' the compost pile. This is an important step as it allows oxygen to access all areas of the compost. Organic material can decompose quicker when oxygen can get to it.

Carbon & Nitrogen:

Compost piles need a good balance of carbon and nitrogen. A good balance is usually achieved by having a mixture of organic material and grass trimmings.

Pests & Diseases:

Composting is a great way of keeping away plant diseases and pests. When composting, you do not need to add store bought fertilizer. Not only can these be expensive, they can also contain harmful chemicals. Through composting any hazardous waste or toxins get naturally removed.

This was a small look at the benefits of composting and combining it with worm farming. So many chemicals and other dangerous items are being placed in our soils which add to pollution. Food scraps and other organic wastes can be used in a natural, healthy way that help the environment. Worm farms, plants, vegetables and animals all can experience an improved life because of composting.

Compared to regular compost, vermicompost contains more antibiotic properties against pathogens and higher amounts of natural plant growth hormones.

-Ed Hubbard-

2

BENEFITS

A worms digestion process helps improve soil. What is truly amazing about this activity is that it all occurs naturally. Nothing harmful or artificial is needed.

More and more gardeners are starting to take advantage of these features with the help of worm farming. In this chapter we will have a quick look at the many benefits it has to offer.

Nature & The Environment

Worm farming is great for our environment, gardens and households. A lot of governments and large corporations are currently producing in a way that releases greenhouse gasses. These gasses contribute to global warming and make the planet more unstable. With composting your organic waste in a worm farm you are actually helping fight these gasses.

It is a way of following nature's natural cycle. Plants and food grow, get consumed and then go back into the earth. *The circle of life*. This allows us to be sure that we do not pollute the earth and our bodies with harmful chemicals.

Recycling

Recycling your organic leftovers with your worm farm is a great way to produce fertilizer and soil conditioner. Worms can turn your recyclables into what's called *vermicast* (worm manure). It helps create super nutrient soil that can produce bigger and healthier fruits, vegetables and plants. Seeds can germinate more effectively and so produce more flowers and fruits.

The produced soil is of excellent quality. There are a lot of chemical fertilizers that can actually burn plants and harm soil. They are also created using the greenhouse gases mentioned above. Worm castings are completely natural and non-toxic. It increases aeration in the soil so air can flow more freely, and it allows soil to retain water better. This means plants will not need as much water to grow. This is extremely beneficial to areas that do not experience as much rainfall and where water is scarce.

Worm castings produce no foul odors and are non toxic. You won't have to worry about any nasty smells coming from all those worm 'droppings'. It is more likely to be a pleasant earthy smell.

Savings & Fun

Owning worms is a lot of fun! Especially for families owning a worm farm is a highlight. Kids will be fascinated with the wiggly, crawling creatures. It is an easy way to teach them more about responsibilities and the environment. It becomes a real treat for everyone.

Parents also won't have to fear having any toxic elements involved with the hobby. Kids or animals won't risk getting hurt. The same cannot be said with chemical fertilizers often used in gardens.

Once you get involved with worm farming you become a part of a new community. It is a lot of fun to exchange ideas with other "farmers" and connect. You are able to share experiences and help one another grow in the hobby or maybe even start a business.

Savings

Worm farming also allows for some hidden savings. Besides the environmental assistance you are providing you can also save on the amount of trash bags you are purchasing. Individuals with large gardens also won't have to worry about buying anymore fertilizer.

Lastly, for those who love to go fishing purchasing bait won't be necessary anymore. Your worm colony will grow quickly! One worm and its offspring can produce over 1500 worms in one year. Many use this excess supply of worms as fish bait.

“

Worms are slimy. In fact, they secrete it and their lubricating fluid contains nitrogen. So they're moving fertilizers. Their slime can also turn your soil into clumps called "aggregates." Aggregates are highly desirable for growing plants.

-Uncle Jim-

3

WHAT WILL YOU NEED

As I mentioned before, anyone can start a worm farm. The hobby is easy to get involved with and the associated costs are not very high. A lot of gardeners are especially attracted to worm farming as it doesn't require a lot of time and it helps other parts of their garden work flourish. Vermicompost will have your plants and vegetables grow bigger and look more vibrant and healthy.

Let's have a quick look at the items you will need to get started. It may surprise you but it is likely that you have many of the items listed below. If not, they are very easy to order online or pick up at your local stores.

Worms

Worms are the center of your farm. They do all the

work needed just by being themselves. A simple life of eating, composting and multiplying. You only need to make sure their environment stays in the correct conditions and the rest is up to them. These slow eaters just need a bit of organic waste and with enough moisture in the soil they will be happy and productive. Red worms and wigglers are usually used for worm farming. In Chapter 4 we will go into more detail explaining what kinds of worms are best for your farm.

The remaining items you will need for your farm all center around what your worms need.

A Simple Container

Most worm farmers opt for a wooden or plastic container. It is usually the best option. Some people use metal containers, but most experts claim this can cause contaminants to get in the compost. This will mess up the worm farming process.

Visually, see through plastic storage bins are great. With whatever container you decide to use, drainage holes will need to be made. This should be done on the sides and bottom of the container. It is also possible to purchase bins online specifically for worm farming. I created a list of containers below, explaining some of positives and negatives that come with each option.

. . .

Plastic (most popular & common option):

- A plastic bin is "non-absorbant" so it will not drain any excess water easily.
- They a very easy to clean.
- May need more drainage holes to prevent the farm from getting too moist.

Wood:

- Wooden bins will absorb a lot of excess water.
- Some drainage holes will need to be added but not very many as it should naturally drain well.
- Keep an eye on the farm becoming too dry.

Metal:

- Metal bins, just like plastic bins are non-absorbent. This makes it harder to drain excess water.
- There are risks of rust and the release of heavy metals with these farms.
- Extra drainage holes will need to be added to help with moisture levels.

Cardboard:

- Cardboard worm farms will absorb a lot of excess water.
- They may fall apart and rot if the moisture levels are too high.

A Cover for the Container

After you decided on a container, you will also need a cover for it. Worms prefer to be in the dark so keeping your farm in a dark area with a cover will allow them to live happily and healthily. The cover can be made out of the same material as your container (e.g. plastic), or can be made out of newspaper or burlap.

Bedding Material - *Newspaper or cardboard.*

The best materials to use for bedding are newspaper and cardboard. You will need to tear it in strips of around 2 inches long. They should be moistened. Alternative options include straw compost, grass clippings, sawdust, dry leaves, burlap and aged manure. Any kinds of 'matte' paper will do. Glossy paper or anything coated with plastic or wax is not a good idea. They can be mixed with harmful toxins that will mess with the composting process.

It is important for the bedding to be set up correctly as the worms depend on it for their food. It should be loose enough that they can breathe and move around in their 'home'.

Organic Waste - *Vegetable & fruit scraps. Degradable items like egg cartons and tea bags are great as well.*

Scraps like the ones mentioned above are great to add to a worm farm. You should be cautious using any waste from animals as they could have contaminants. This could allow unwanted pests to breed in your farm and damage the ecosystem you are creating. We will go into more detail describing exactly what is safe to place in your farm and what is not in Chapter 5 - Food & Feeding.

Worms are 90% water. In comparison, humas are about 75% water.

-Wormfarmguru.com-

4

WHICH WORMS?

The highlight of having a worm farm is, well, the worms of course.

So what kind of worms should I use?

It is actually possible to head outside and collect some worms. It is best to head into a forest like area after some rain and dig some up. Not all worms are as good for composting, however. The common earth worm for example is not an effective composter. They like to dig down deeper in the earth and your farm will probably not be very deep. You can identify these guys by their length and color. Common earth worms are relatively long and look pale. It is helpful to have the right kinds of worms 'working' on the farm. Let's have a look at some popular choices.

Red (Wigglers):

Eisenia foetida/andrei 2"-4"

Red worms are great for worm farms. They are often called 'red wigglers' because, well they wiggle! They love spending time more at the "surface" of the earth which is perfect for composting.

Red Wigglers reproduce easily and they provide the earth with plenty of nutrients. They are also a durable worm species as they can withstand different temperatures and confined spaces. Red Wigglers are able to process a lot of waste materials and that allows for a lot of soil to be enriched.

European Nightcrawler:

Eisenia hortensis 3"-8"

This is another worm species that is frequently used for worm farming. They are a popular live bait, so they can often be found as bird or fish feed. European Nightcrawlers can also assist with composting.

. . .

Red Earthworms:

Lumbricus rubellus 1"-4"

Most *red* worms are usually a good option for composting. Red earthworms are very similar to wigglers but they are usually a little bit smaller. They are durable and able to survive a cold winter and are also a popular option for worm farming.

Blue Worms:

Perionyx excavatus 1"-3"

Blue worms are a shorter and chubbier species of worm. They are more commonly found in tropical areas. This makes them a great option when you live in an area where temperatures are often above 86 degrees Fahrenheit.

African Nightcrawlers:

Eudrilus eugeniae 6"-8"+

African nightcrawlers are the largest worms I will mention. They can compost the most as they are the biggest, and they are a good option for tropical climates.

The worms mentioned above are great for farms and in gardens. They are good options to fertilize and enrich the soil. There are thousands of earthworm species, however the ones mentioned above are most commonly used for vermicomposting. They are easy to get and are available as either youngsters or adults. It is even possible to purchase eggs. There are often several worms in an egg.

Worms are the most important part of a worm farm. They are what makes the system go and a farm a success.

There are about one million species of worm.

-DK *Science*-

5

FOOD & FEEDING

So what kinds of food and waste can you add to your worm farm?

Worms thrive when they are fed a mixture of carbon and nitrogen. This helps create a well-balanced system and allows for the farm to produce at maximum capacity. So what does this actually mean? Carbon can be found in things like shredded paper, cardboard and newspaper. Nitrogen is found in food scraps like organic fruits and vegetables.

It turns out that worms have quite the appetite for mostly all raw vegan dishes. All 'green' matter is warmly welcomed on the farm. Animal products like meat, bones or dairy should not find their way on the menu. They are usually not consumed by worms and they pose a higher risk for containing contaminants for the farm.

Many beginners believe that they need to grind down the food or waste they place in their farms. This isn't necessary as the microorganisms in a container will already help soften and break everything down. The composting process can however be be sped up by chopping up the scraps. Many beginners will also find that certain seeds will start to sprout out of their farms. If you do not mind these growing, then there is no issue but if it is a problem, simply make sure to chop up seeds before placing them inside.

An important thing to remember is that you should not add too much food waste. Adding too much food forms a mixture that is not good for the worms to eat. It also creates foul odors and increases the risk for pests taking over your farm. This should not scare you off, however. Most households end up not having enough waste to feed their thriving worm communities. Luckily, worm populations adjust to the environment they are in. They adapt and population growth stays at a consistent level. We will look more into this in Chapter 9 - Controlling Population.

It is great to stir the mixture of worm food. This allows for oxygen to spread throughout the farm and you will be able to better asses moisture levels. If the mixture is too moist, add more bedding and paper scraps. If the mixture is too dry, add some water. Many owners also add some garden soil to their farms which provides worms the help they need to better digest the food waste.

There are 2 techniques when it comes down to feeding:

1. Top Feeding

This is a very simple process. You just place the organic matter right on top of the current layer of bedding. Then there is typically another layer of bedding placed over this. This system is repeated every time feeding takes place.

2. Pocket Feeding

Pocket feeding is a great way to prevent overfeeding your worm farm. It is a technique where you add just a small amount of food scraps under some bedding in a section of the farm. A few days later a farmer will rotate the bin and do the same thing in a different section. This process repeats until all areas of the bin are used. This gives the worms a chance properly decompose pockets of food without large areas of food spoiling.

. . .

It is great to use a combination of both methods. Also, always consider covering food scraps with bedding material. Fruit flies and parasites will be attracted to exposed fruits and food wastes.

Let's have a look at some of the things that are great additions to your farm.

Great Things to Compost in Your Farm

- Vegetable Left Overs and Peels
- Potato Peels
- Fruit Left Overs
- Moldy Bread
- Coffee Grounds
- Paper Filters
- Tea Bags
- Egg Shells
- Cardboard and Egg Cartons
- Leaves
- Horse and Cow Manure

Surprisingly Also

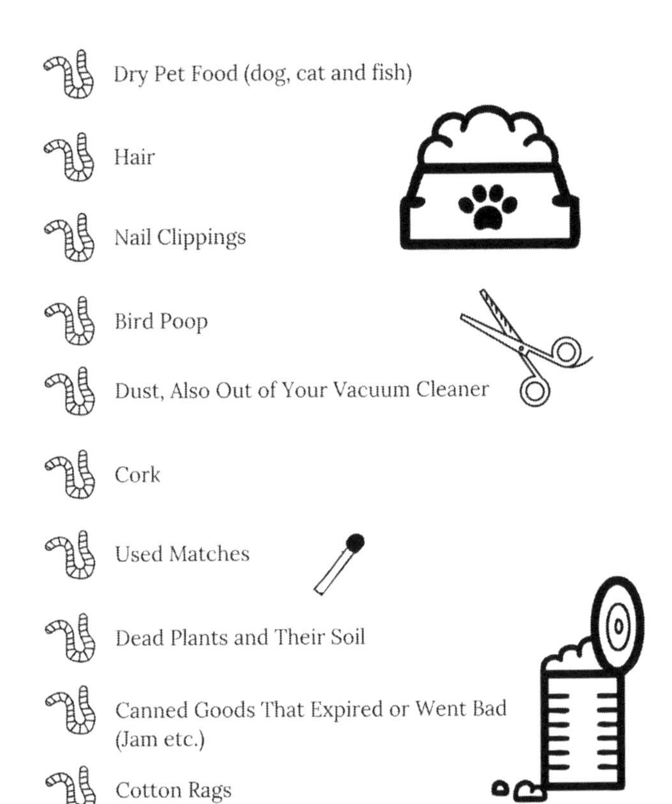

- Dry Pet Food (dog, cat and fish)
- Hair
- Nail Clippings
- Bird Poop
- Dust, Also Out of Your Vacuum Cleaner
- Cork
- Used Matches
- Dead Plants and Their Soil
- Canned Goods That Expired or Went Bad (Jam etc.)
- Cotton Rags

What to Compost in Moderation

Banana Peels

These rot quite quickly and this can put your farm at risk. Also, it is best to place only organic wastes in your farm. Non-organic waste can have pesticides that can kill off the entire bin.

Citrus Fruit

These fruit have strong smells and tastes which worms dislike. I recommend for you not to add these to your farms but in a well-running system minor additions are fine.

Onions and Garlic

These also have strong smells and tastes. They are okay in moderation in healthy farms.

Tomatoes

They are quite acidic and can only be added in moderation.

Do Not Place These in Your Worm Farm

Meat, Bones and Fat
These spoil fast and put your farm at risk.

Dairy Products
Milk, butter and cheese all spoil fast and are not good options to add.

Pineapple and Papaya
They contain enzymes that kill worms.

Highly Salty and Spicy Food
This will kill your worms.

Grass Clippings
This can be sprayed with pesticides which will kill your worms.

Glossy Paper or Colored Ink Paper
Will kill your worms.

Oils and Fats
Worms breathe through their skin. Oils make this difficult or prevent it from happening. Anything that is very greasy should be avoided.

Soap
Will kill your worms.

Canned Sauces
They spoil quickly and mess up the moisture content of a farm.

Peanut Butter
Will kill your worms.

Non-Biodegradable Items
Plastics, metal and glass are all no good for your farm.

Vinegar
Highly acidic and will kill your worms.

Each worm will eat 20 ounces of matter per year.

-Ed Hubbard-

6

FARM DESIGN

As we mentioned before you won't need a lot of space to start a worm farm. Even if you live in a small apartment without a balcony, the hobby is feasible. If you have a safe area for a small container, you are good to go!

There are several ways to go about setting up your farm. The easiest thing to do is to start it on the ground. Larger concepts use a concrete pad, but as a start having a container on the ground is perfect.

Once you are considering expansion, you can think about creating "windrows". Larger worm farms are organized in this manner. Windrows are long rows of worm farms. It allows you to have a well-organized overview of the farm and fertilize more soil.

The system works by placing the worms in the first row.

They will leave castings there and then continue on with the second row, and so forth. The worms stay in the correct row because 'farmers' will use bricks or wooden boards to keep them enclosed.

When starting out with your first container it is important not to forget your cover. You will need to have one on there to shade the area. Worms aren't fans of light and they will produce better in areas that are dark and moist.

For the most part, you can be quite creative with designing your worm farm. How you organize it is all about preference and availability of space. Feel free to test out different settings. If you wish not to make your own design, it is possible to purchase ready made options. There are countless options that can be used inside your home, apartment or garden. Many with homes choose to set up in the basement. There is plenty of space and you can control the environment.

I have seen fellow enthusiasts have small farms under their kitchen sink. It works very well as it stays mostly dark and it is a simple process to place organic waste there.

Worms breathe through their skin. Air dissolves on the mucus of their skin, so they must stay moist to breathe.

-Journeynorth.org-

7

SMALL & LARGE SCALE FARMS

Worm farming can be started in a small area and so at a tiny scale. It can also however, take place at a large scale. Usually large scale worm farms are reserved for those looking to build a business. What is true for all farms small or large is that the bedding needs to remain moist for the worms. If you live in a very sunny or hot environment, you should try to keep your farm out of direct sunlight. It will be possible to add waste daily or weekly. This all depends on your needs and how much waste you and your family generate.

Another fact for all farms small or large is that when your worms first begin to eat, they will consume around half of their own weight. Slowly, as they continue to get accustomed to their environment, they will increase their consumption until they eat up to all of their weight. I recommend giving your worms some time to consume the waste before adding any new food to your farm. It is possible to place new food in a separate area of your bin or farm. This way there isn't a large pile forming in a specific spot that will not get digested properly.

Now that we looked at some general themes that all farms should consider, lets see some differences between small-scale and large-scale farms.

Small-Scale Farms

Many beginners start with worm farms on a smaller scale. This is simply due to the ease of the hobby and low costs. I recommend beginners and those with small farms to still invest in a collection tray. This tray should be placed underneath the container for drainage. As mentioned before all containers will have drainage holes. Having a collection tray can prevent messes and spills. Plastic bins will have a lot more drainage than wooden ones. Wooden containers will absorb a lot of the moisture and liquids that trickle down.

When it comes to setting up a small-scale farm, there are generally three ways to move forward.

1. Continuous Vertical Flow:

This is the most beginner friendly system for worm bins. Trays or bins are stacked *vertically* up on one another. It becomes an easier task to regulate moisture levels as there is a very straightforward drainage system. There are generally a minimum of 3 levels to the farm.

- The lowest layer collects drainage and the worm tea.
- The layer above this is the first compartment that gets filled with waste.
- The top layer is initially empty and covered up.

The two upper trays have a mesh screens at their bottoms. This allows for both drainage and the worms to move from one layer to the next. The process begins by filling up the middle layer with scraps until it is full. The worms will get to work and begin breaking everything down. After the layer is full, you can move on to filling up the tray above it. As the worms finish breaking down the layer they are in, they will slowly move up through the mesh to the upper layer to find more food. This is how the process continues and recycles.

Continuous Vertical Flow Example

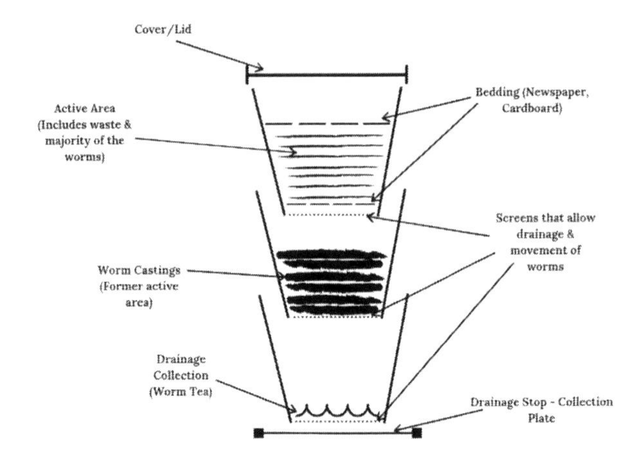

2. Continuous Horizontal Flow:

This is another way individuals commonly set up their worm farm. Simply put, the system consists of a large container that is split in the middle by a mesh. It should be noted that this setup is for the more 'advanced' farmer. It is more challenging to monitor the moisture levels in a container like this.

The principles of this setup are very similar to that of the 'vertical flow', the system is is just laid down. One side of the container is filled with scraps and waste.

After this side is filled, you switch over to the other side. Your worms will follow the food and crawl to the newly filled spot.

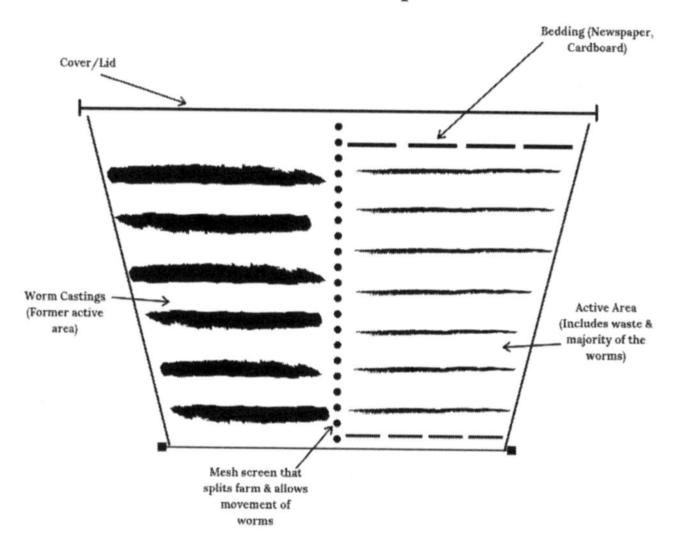

3. Non-continuous:

The last setup we will look at is a non-continuous one. The systems we look at before all have a process of the worms moving towards a new area. This way you will be able to scoop up worm castings and fertilized soil without picking out worms. The worms are *continuously* moving into a specific area. A non-continuous setup uses a single container.

The breakdown inside the container goes as followed:

- The bottom will have bedding that is used as liner.
- On top of the liner will be organic matter used for composting.
- The top layer is another layer of bedding.

This is the smallest set up you can create. It can be very effective and space efficient however, when it's time to harvest you will need to empty everything. This means separating the worms and all the materials in your farm.

Non-Continuous Example

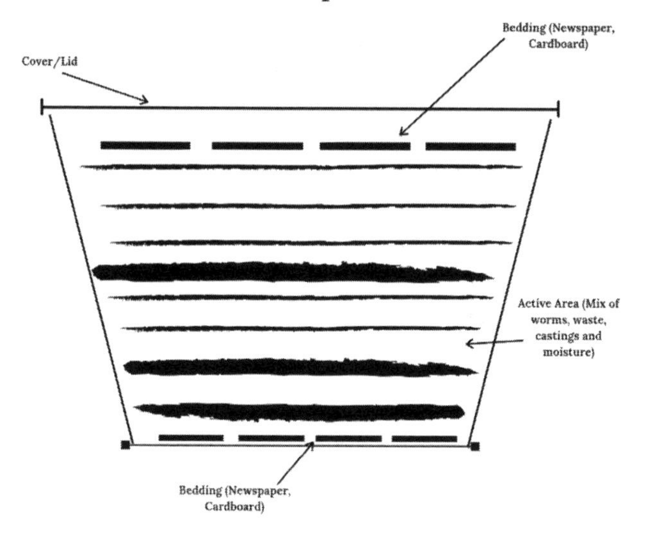

Now that we understand how smaller worm farms are organized, we can see how the system works on a larger scale.

Large Scale

Building a large worm farm is usually reserved for individuals looking to build a business with their farm. There are two common ways for setting everything up.

. . .

1. Windrows

A windrow is most commonly used for building a large scale worm farm. It is a very simple process that is all natural, and the worms still do most of the work. There are very low star-up costs involved and you will not need any special training.

So how does it work?

A windrow is a long row of material that can vary in length depending on available space, that is 5-10 feet wide and up to 3 feet high. The material of a windrow comprises of some bedding and then on top of this manure solids and other organic waste. Worms are added to the mix and every week a new layer of waste and manure is added as well. This gradually increases the depth of the windrow and farmers will need to carefully assess moisture levels along with temperature of the farm.

Some farmers will find it easier to set up their farms on concrete or other hard surfaces. This way during wet weather it becomes easier to protect and control your farm.

Farmers using the windrow system will extend piles after it reaches to around 3 feet in thickness. A new layer is created directly next to and against the first row. Your worms will migrate to the new fresh food and manure. After about 3-6 months the first windrow will be ready for harvesting and farmers will be able to use and sell the fine soil that has been created.

2. Raised Flow Through Systems

A raised system simply consists of raised worm beds. It takes advantage of the fact that worms generally prefer to remain closer to the surface of where they live. They will also move closer to the newest food source, which leaves a high concentration of their castings behind. Thus, a raised flow through system signifies large beds with grates at the bottom. A farmer will continue to set up organic waste and manure at the top of the bed, which the worms will break down.

After an initial priming period, vermicompost can be removed every day as it falls through the spaces underneath the bed. A bar situated towards the bottom of the bed also assists the movement of earth and allows compost to move downwards more easily. Worms will generally remain at the top, however it is possible that some move downwards as well.

This system is better used indoors and it a great choice for farmers in warm weather conditions.

Composting worms can eat up to their body weight on a daily basis.

-Ed Hubbard-

8

VERMI-COMPOSTING

We briefly looked at vermicomposting earlier, but it describes the entire process of organic composting with worms. Using this process of combining natural food wastes with your worm farm creates the best soil. All the nutrients transfer into the soil making it the ultimate fertilizer.

Red wigglers are one of the more popular worms for vermicomposting. They are naturally found in Europe and the United States. Red Wigglers are great at breaking down elements in compost and manure piles.

So what elements and properties are involved?

Vermicompost has a lot of microbial life. 'Microbes' are any microscopic organisms. This means minute living organisms like bacteria, fungi and other cells. They help nutrients to be broken down in the soil and turn into a form available for plants. Vermicompost also contains a lot of 'mucus'.

The mucus is nice and sticky, and this allows nutrients to stick in the soil. Without it, any rain would wash away all the benefactors. It is also the reason vermicompost retains moisture so well. All in all, fruits and seed pits love these qualities and it allows them to grow very well. It is common for little seeds from your organic waste to grow out. This means tomatoes and eggplants will look to grow within a few weeks.

As an overview, using Vermicompost in your worm farm has the following main advantages:

- Rich soil
- Excellent water retention
- Enhanced root growth
- Improved structure
- Better physical look for fruits, vegetables and plants

So how can we harvest this nutrient rich soil for our plants?

It will take around 5-7 months before you are able to harvest your worm compost for the first time. After this first composting period the process will speed up and you will be able to harvest some compost every month. The amount you can harvest depends on the size of your farm and how many worms you have working.

Harvesting is completed by simply extracting worm castings (the nutrient-rich "*black gold*") from your farm without also extracting a lot of worms. The most efficient way to do this depends on how your farm is designed.

Let's explore some of the more common ways worm castings are harvested...

Natural Worm Relocation Techniques

The most popular and common way to harvest involves "encouraging" your worms to move. If your farm is organized in a continuous flow system (vertical or horizontal) this process has already been simplified. In these systems worms will look to migrate towards food.

This means they will naturally move from an area of the farm that is ready to be harvested and can be separated.

If the system you are using does not include multiple trays, it is still possible to encourage your worms to 'relocate'. Collect all the un-composted scraps and most them to one area of your farm. Place all your fresh food only in the spot you want the worms to move to. Depending on the size of your farm in around 1-4 weeks your worms will have migrated to your desired area. You will now be able to harvest worm free soil.

*Brothers Green Tip: It is normal for some worms to get lost and remain in soil you are looking to harvest. Just put them back in your farm with the rest or place them in the garden with your natural plant fertilizer. Make sure there aren't too many worms in the soil you are harvesting. You will still need enough of them to work on your farm.

Light Relocation Technique

Worms despise the light and some worm farmers use this to their advantage when they want to harvest castings. You can apply artificial light to a specific section of your farm. This will drive the worms deeper down in the farm or to areas that are dark. You will quickly have an area that is mostly worm free, and that is ready for harvesting.

Please be cautious with this technique. Never expose your worms to excessive heat. It risks drying up your worms and killing them. Using too much light can also dry out your farm and mess with the moisture balance.

Hand Technique

This is the simplest technique when it comes to harvesting. You may already have an idea of how it works but it simply entails getting your hands “dirty”. Just dig down towards the bottom of your farm and grab a handful of vermicompost. That is basically it. You can pick out worms if they are in the mix or you can add the entire mixture to your garden.

It is also possible to create something called ‘worm tea’ from vermicompost. In combination with water it becomes a great liquid fertilizer. Worm tea is the liquid concentrate of vermicompost. Essentially all the minerals and nutrients are extracted from the solid compost and transferred into the ‘tea’. It produces all of the same benefits it is just in a concentrated form. We will go over this and *compost tea* in greater detail in Chapter 11.

Worms increase the water holding capacity of the soil.

-Peter Rutherford-

9

CONTROLLING POPULATION

Worms in your farm are simultaneous hermaphrodites. This means that each worm has both the male and female reproductive organs. As you can imagine, it makes them very efficient when it comes to reproduction and it ensures the species continued survival. If the conditions in a farm are healthy and balanced, it is common for worm populations to double almost every 60 days.

When worms are sexually mature, they grow an elongated bulbous section on their bodies.

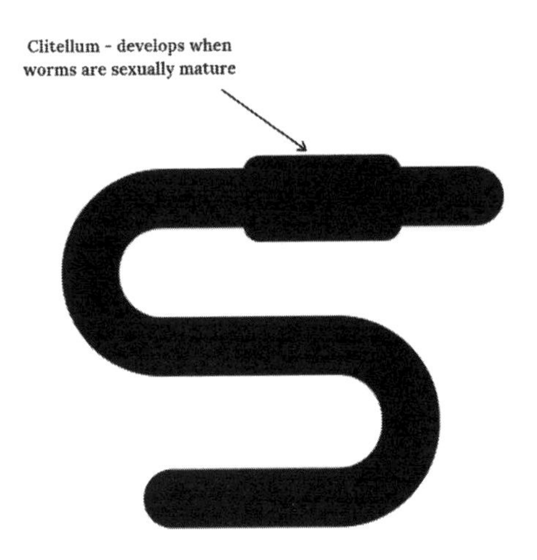

After this structure is developed worms are able to produce 2-3 worm cacoons (eggs) every week. These eggs take around 11 weeks to hatch, and red worms grow sexually mature at around 3 months old. In healthy environments, populations explode quickly.

With populations growing so rapidly, won't it be easy for my farm to be overrun?

Worms are relatively good at balancing out production.

They adjust to their environment and at a certain point the groups population growth stops and remains at a constant level.

Population is controlled by 3 main factors:

1. Availability of Food

When worms are fed on a regular basis in a contained space they adjust to taking in a specific amount of nutrients. As reproduction takes place, more worms will struggle to get food and more food will need to be added to the equation.

2. Space Requirements

Space plays a large role in worm population. As the amount of worms and food increase more space will also be necessary. It is common for farm owners to have to change soil and locations more frequently as the population grows. This keeps everything fresh.

3. The Environment

If a farm becomes overpopulated, there is a risk for the environment to become toxic. Moisture will not drain properly and worms will look to leave to new areas.

These all cause a worm population to adjust and either increase or decrease. Once the worms in your farm have had the time to acclimate to their environment, they will eventually regulate their population output.

Worms have 5 hearts.

-Journeynorth.org-

10

ISSUES & TROUBLE SHOOTING

Worm farming is generally a low intensive activity. The worms get to do most of the work, although that only means eating, pooping and multiplying. There are some common issues you may run into with your farm, however. Some farmers find they have problems like a smelly bin, bug invasions and worms escaping. I will look to provide not only solutions but also explain what may have caused the issues.

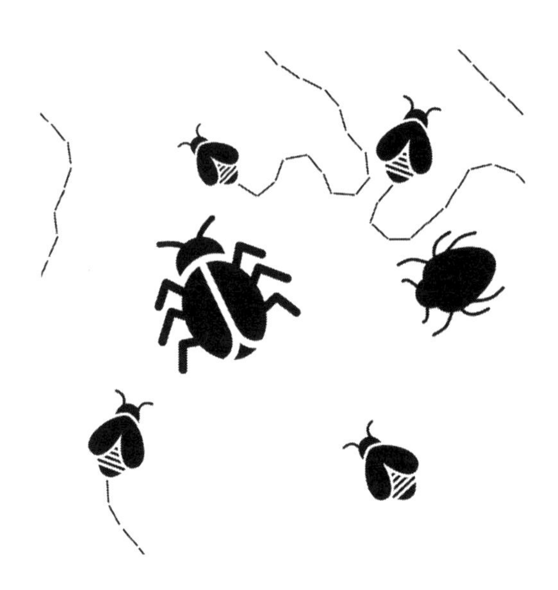

Fruit Flies, Insects & Other Pests

How come?

It is common for worm farmers to have some fruit flies flying around their farms. This is usually the case when worms are overfed, or when there are a lot of exposed food scraps. The more food there is exposed and available the larger the chance flies and insects will be attracted to it.

At times, ants may also find a worm farm an attractive place to get food. Besides exposed food the ants can also be attracted by dry soil in the container.

In Chapter 5 we looked at what you should and shouldn't place in a worm farm. Often, farmers accidentally place meat scraps in their containers. This can also attract bugs and will allow maggots to grow.

Some worm farmers have their farm outdoors. This allows for other pests like rodents to be attracted to compostable wastes. Rats, mice and other small animals can possibly find their way in your farm and look to take advantage of easy meals.

Possible Solutions

Your worm farm should have a tight lid at the top. This will prevent a lot of pests from getting inside and causing contamination. To stop fruit flies many farmers bury all the food scraps, and some have a fly trap nearby. It is also recommended to feed the farm a little less. This decreases the time food is openly available for insects and other pests.

If ants are an issue, I recommend pouring some water and lime into the soil or where they are congregating. This increase in moisture will discourage them from staying. Another tip is if your farm has legs to put some vaseline on them. This will keep the ants from climbing up.

Maggots will be a rare issue since your farm shouldn't contain meat. If they are present get rid of the meat and place a piece of bread soaked in milk in the farm. The maggots will stick to the bread, and then it will be easier to remove all of them.

If you find rodents in your farm, many of the same preventative measure can be taken. A sealed worm bin can help along with a reduction of food waste. All food scraps should be covered with bedding. If the problem persists the only remaining option may be to move the farm indoors.

The Farm Smells Bad

How come?

Just like overfeeding and exposed food scraps can attract bugs it can also bring out some nasty smells. When food is left in the open for too long, and there is too much for the worms to compost it will start to rot and stink.

Another possible cause for foul smells is when your farm contains too much liquid and it does not drain properly. Air flow may be restricted as there is too much moisture.

Possible Solutions

Bad smells can be fixed by feeding less and covering all food scraps with plenty of bedding. Similarly to when bugs are invading the farm, exposed food will also attract nasty scents.

If the farm is too wet, you can try draining off excess liquid. Some owners will add more draining holes to their container. I also recommend mixing dry bedding through the farm. This will help absorb a lot of the excess moisture and stop nasty smells.

You may have accidentally placed some food scraps in the farm that aren't appropriate. Too many banana peels, dairy products and meat will quickly allow for rough smells to make their way out of the farm. Simply remove the smelly object and mix in some fresh bedding.

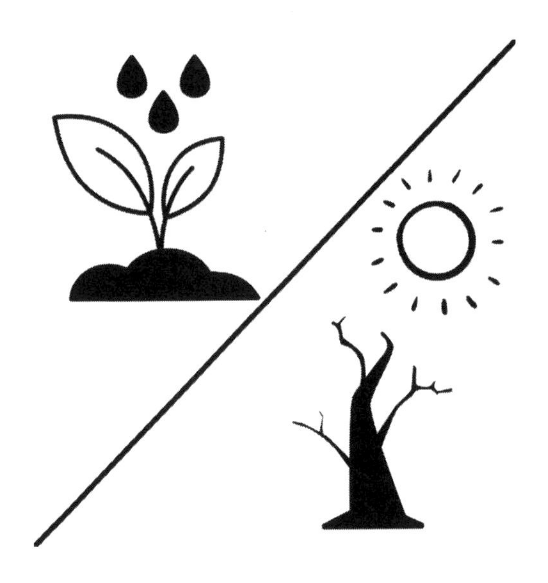

The Farm is Too Wet or Dry

How come?

One of the more important aspects of worm farming is mastering moisture levels. In order to have a properly thriving farm there needs to be a proper balance of wetness and dryness. A farm that is too wet will smell bad and can 'drown' your worms. A farm that is too dry will attract pests and can also kill your worms.

Wet Farms:

A farm is usually wet because it isn't able to drain properly. Moisture is not able to escape or run through the farm and it simply builds up. It can also be due to overfeeding. Too much wet food waste is added and the farms size cannot keep up with composting it properly. Lastly, airflow may be getting restricted. The farm can be too compact and so air and moisture is not able to drain out of the farm.

Dry Farms:

On the other end of the spectrum are worm farms that are overly dry. This is usually because of too much dry bedding. It can absorb much of the moisture that the farm requires. It may also be a cause of too much air flow or ventilation. Similarly to when you hang out clothes to dry. We spread them out so they can 'breathe' and they dry faster. If there is too much airflow in your farm, it will also dry out.

Possible Solutions

Mastering moisture levels depends on many factors. Where you live and where your farm is located all play a role. Here are my recommendations if your farm is...

Wet:

Add more drain and ventilation holes. This will allow more air to run through your farm and let moisture run through it more smoothly. It can also be helpful to mix more dry bedding through the farm. The bedding will absorb a lot of excess liquids. If excess moisture is because of too much feeding, then make sure to feed the worms less.

Dry:

Add some water to the farm by lightly sprinkling it or spraying it with a spray water bottle. I have found it helpful to add wet newspaper to the top of the farm, after watering the farm lightly. The newspaper will be somewhat of a 'moisture blanket'.

Worms are Leaving the Farm or Dying

How come?

It is very rare of your worms to try and leave the farm. They love being in dark, moist areas and these are the conditions of your farm. Outside of the farm it's bright and dry. This means things have to get pretty bad for them to want to leave.

*__Brothers Green Note__: There is no need to panic if a couple of worms escape from your farm. It is normal for some to get lost and accidentally leave.

Worms will look to leave if it gets too hot or cold for them. Worms die if they are exposed to temperatures over 86 degrees Fahrenheit and cannot tolerate temperatures below 55 degrees Fahrenheit for very long. It is important to keep a sharp eye on the temperature and your farm during the summer and winter months. If you see an increase in worms looking to escape, it is due to uncomfortable temperatures.

Worms will also look for a new location if the population grew too large for the farm or if there is not enough food to support everyone. Experts mention that if they cannot properly eat for over 4 weeks, they will look to move. If the farm is too busy, it is normal for worms to look for new areas.

A common beginner mistake farmers make is to put too many non-organic items in their farm. These items may contain pesticides and other harmful matter that can kill worms. If your worms are able to survive, they may still look to escape. A more minor version of this occurs when the farm contains too many items worms don't like. Citrus fruits, garlic, onions and other items with strong flavors or smells will make worms look to flee.

Possible Solutions

Here you will need to identify why your worms may be leaving or dying and then correct the conditions in the farm. If it is too hot, try to move the container to a cooler area (A unit with an A/C or in a cool basement). If your farm is indoors, it is unlikely for conditions to get too cold. If you the farm needs to be warmed up some farmers wrap a blanket around it.

*__Brothers Green Note__: To get your worms to travel deeper down the farm you can shine a light on the surface. Worms hate the light and will travel deeper down to avoid it. This can help when worms are accidentally finding their way out of the top of the farm.

Worms can regenerate. If you cut a worm, it sometimes grows back that section of itself. It depends on where it is cut. In that respect they're also like a lizard, which can regrow a new tail, and starfish, which can grow back an arm.

-Uncle Jim-

11

COMPOSTING & COMPOST TEA

My focus for this book is specifically 'worm farming'. I understand that some readers may be thrown off by owning hundreds or maybe even thousands of worms. Taking care of that many pet worms is easy but can be a turn off for some. This is why I wanted to also offer a small introduction to what is possible composting wise without worms. It takes a bit longer, but the activity also has a great amount of benefits.

Composting itself has many benefits. They are very similar to the benefits of worm farming, it just doesn't require the responsibility of taking care of lots of wiggly friends. Benefits include:

- Reduced waste that goes to landfills
- Reduced methane emissions from landfills

- Enriched soil
- Reduced need for harmful chemical fertilizers

Composting is generally completed outside however it is possible to get the job indoors as well. There are 3 main ingredients in compost pile. These are browns, greens and water.

Browns

Browns are organic material that are no longer alive such as branches, twigs and dead leaves.

Greens

Greens are you and your family's food and organic wastes. It is material like vegetable waste, fruit scraps, grass clippings, coffee grounds and tea bags.

Water

Similarly to how your worm form needs the correct amount of moisture, a regular compost pile needs the same treatment.

It is best to find a shady, dry spot to start your compost pile. Next you simply create a pile of the brown and green materials mentioned above. You will need to regularly mix, turn and water the pile. Overtime, as more material is added you will find that the material at the bottom has turned into dark and rich soil. This soil is then ready to use as plant fertilizer. The process can take anywhere between 3 months to some years.

Compost Tea & Worm Tea

Compost tea is considered 'liquid gold' by many gardeners. It is a powerful natural fertilizer that helps create high quality plants, vegetables and fruits. The 'tea' is full of nutrients and minerals that give plants greener leaves, bigger blooms and creates healthier crops. With both a worm farm and a compost pile you will be able to make this special 'juice'.

A simple way to create compost tea is as followed -

1. Fill up a bucket to around 1/3rd of its size with quality finished compost. This can come from either your worm farm or compost pile.

2. Add water to the top of the bucket

3. Let the mixture sit for around 4 days stirring it now and then.

4. Strain the mixture through an old shirt or other fabric into another bucket. You can place the remaining solid earth back in your worm farm or compost pile.

5. Dilute your 'tea' with water so that it is the color of

weak tea. Your tea is now ready to use and you can water the base of your plants or vegetables with the liquid gold.

Worms do not have eyes or ears but they have "receptor cells" that can detect light and vibrations.

-Journeynorth.org-

12

WORM FARMING AS A BUSINESS

Starting and developing a worm farm is a lot of fun. Many hobbyists gradually transition from owning a farm for fun or for the environmental benefits to starting a side 'hustle'. The hobby easily turns into a passion and it can be a great way to make a bit of extra money or depending on your goals, a full-fledged business.

So how do you go about starting something like this?

In this chapter I will explain how you can potentially get started with worm farming as a business. My goal is to give you a great general guide with getting started. The aim was not to overwhelm you with a complex business plan but to provide you with actionable steps to follow and hopefully find success. One thing to note, I am not a financial or business expert. I used my own experience and research to give the best advice possible, but please meet with the appropriate advisors before starting any business venture.

Before Starting

It is best to have a full understanding of worm farming before looking to start a business. I recommend for you to first practice the hobby for some time. It is important to be able to set everything up correctly and have some experience with things that may go wrong. Of course, unforeseen problems will still come up but you will have a good general idea of what to expect and how to react.

It is good to have experienced all the seasons as a worm farmer and the climate change this brings. This way you can best predict and prepare your business. Your confidence will grow and you can truly call yourself an expert in vermiculture.

You will have the experience and know exactly how quickly your farm population can grow. How to maintain the correct moisture levels for your environment. How much vermicompost you can generate. This and more are all essential things to know if you want to turn this hobby into a business. Your knowledge will in turn also reflect back to your customers. They will feel secure with purchasing from you as you know exactly what you are talking about.

Make a Plan

After gaining experience in the activity, it's time for laying down the blueprint. My recommendation here is to clearly define to yourself -

1. Why do I want to start the business?

and

2. What are my goals?

You may want to start a business to help the environment. It may be because you would like to have a little more money for family vacations or to help around the household. You may want to build a huge company that changes the way people purchase their fertilizer. There is no wrong answer, but it is essential to figure this out before getting started.

Once you know your 'why' and have your goals you can start making a plan. Even if your goals are very small and you only want to have a little 'side hustle' it is great to make a business plan. It forces you to clearly map out critical things like; What supplies do I need, and how much space will I need to run the operation?

Here are some things I recommend you to keep in mind:

- **Supplies** - Containers | Bedding Materials | Food & Organic waste | Tools
- **Space** - Indoors | Outdoors | Rent Extra Space
- **A Team** - Will you work by yourself or will you build a team.
- **Your Offer** - What are you looking to provide? Vermicompost, worms, compost tea or a combination of things.
- **Finances** - Assess your finances. Consider your expenses and consider your potential profits.

It is important to consider all the costs of starting a business. Worm farming is a relatively cheap activity but depending on what level you plan on operating on, there will be costs. I always like to overestimate on costs. Often unforeseen expenses come up, an overestimated budget will cancel these out.

Legal Structure

Legal structure is incredibly important when starting a

business. It affects everything from your liability if something goes wrong to how you file taxes. It is crucial that you meet with the appropriate advisors for this step. Depending on where you live you will need to have a valid business license. It may also be necessary to meet certain requirements or have a permit to sell worms and fertilizer. It should be relatively easy to meet with a professional and discuss these options.

There are generally two business structures most worm farmers start with.

1. Sole Proprietorship or a Partnership

If you plan on owning the entire business by yourself and being responsible for all debts and obligations, then a simple structure is a sole proprietorship. The main risk with this format is you are personally liable if something goes wrong. Someone can sue you directly and not the business. It is however a very simple structure to organize. You will also be able to discuss different insurances that can help cover you and limiting risk.

A partnership has all the same characteristics as a sole proprietorship but the assets and liabilities are divided into two parts or more. This can be helpful as you do not have to work by yourself and you can find a business partner with complimentary skills.

. . .

2. Limited Liability Corporation

The other most common structure for small businesses is an LLC. This formation allows for many of the same tax benefits of a partnership or sole proprietorship however you are no longer personally liable.

Your companies structure all depends on how you plan on operating your business. Trust a professional with your goals and vision and they will advise you on the best options available.

Marketing & Advertising

After you have set up your services and product, it is time to get customers. Unfortunately, this can be quite a challenging task. Just because you have a great product available, customers will not immediately line up to purchase. I listed some great ways to get started with advertising your business below. Some are free and require very little investment. If you hope to grow your business, it is important to see these costs as investment.

Word of Mouth

If people are not aware you have a product to sell, they

won't even know to consider purchasing from you. I recommend for you to let your friends and family know your worm farm is open for business! People often underestimate how supportive their friends and family can be. Not only will some of them purchase from you for their own plants or vegetables, they will also tell their friends if they are happy. People are more eager than ever to support smaller businesses. Make sure to let people know what you offer and explain the benefits. You can evolve to getting some simple business cards made and hand some out when your worm farm comes up in conversation.

Flyers

This is a simple and cheap way to advertise what your farm has to offer. Create a simple design explaining the benefits of purchasing from you and print it out at home. Hand them out at different events where potential customers will be. Vegetable markets and farmer's markets are a great place to start.

Connections

Connections are very important when it comes to success in business. Try to develop relationships with other local businesses, plant shops or nurseries. Show them your product and offer them a good deal to supply your products in their shops. They can already have large customer bases that may be interested in what you offer. These connections can grow and who knows, perhaps one day you can supply a large chain with their fertilizer.

Online presence

Today, if your business is not online you are losing out on a lot of potential customers. It will be very helpful to create social media profiles on platforms like Facebook and Instagram. You can show customers how cool and helpful your business is and notify them of a sale or where to purchase. The platforms are free to post on and even a small advertising budget with them can go a long way.

You can also place free advertisements online on websites like Craigslist. Those looking to take their businesses to the next level can also consider getting a website made and spending money on online advertising.

Other Paid Sources

You may have big plans for your worm farm business. It can then be helpful to organize an advertising budget. You will then be able to allocate funds for advertising in local newspapers, television and billboards. There are a lot of paid options for advertising your products and services.

It is important to enjoy the process and to continue working on growing your business. Keep in mind why you started the business and follow the plan you laid out. I want to encourage you not to stress when things don't happen how you hope. Simply adjust course and keep going. Some businesses take longer than other to get started. So have fun with it and eventually success will come.

The average lifespan of a worm is about 2 years, but they can live up to as long as 8 years.

-Wormfarmguru.com-

13

TIPS & IDEAS FOR SUCCESS

We looked at a variety of topics regarding worm farming. We observed which worms to use and how to feed and care for them. We considered different design elements of creating your farm and even dealt with the potential of starting a business. With this, I wanted to make sure we covered some general tips and reminders for successfully running your worm farm.

The aim is to hopefully help beginners a lot and give seasoned farmers some beneficial new ideas. The points below are not structured in a specific order from most important to least important. I simply let my mind flow free and the results are my thoughts written down. They are things that would have been great to know when I started worm farming and what I try to keep in mind today...

... Enjoy!

Location, location, location! No, worm farming differs greatly from real estate but the hobby does require you to consider location. You should not place your farm in an area where the temperature greatly fluctuates or where it is either too hot or cold. Worms are more sensitive than we realize and so should not be in an area with a lot of vibrations and noise. Place your farm in a location that is fairly calm and pleasingly cool.

Food control. Keep an eye on how much you are feeding your worms. As the population increases, they will need more food.

Moisture levels. The soil in your farm should always have a good level of moisture to it. It is important to find a proper balance. If the soil gets too wet, add newspaper. In general, it is better for the farm to be a tad too wet than too dry.

Population growth of worms. As the population of your farm grows and get excessive, you may want to create a new farm. It is easy to duplicate the process and you can maintain it the same way.

Side income opportunities. If you have some extra worms that you don't need, check with suppliers to see if they would be interested in buying some from you.

Bedding. Always place enough paper and/or cardboard in your farm. This allows oxygen to circulate and get to the food scraps.

Bad smells. If your farm smells, try to find the source. In most cases it will only be necessary to add some more bedding to your farm. It may however come from a specific source that shouldn't be in the farm.

Balancing food levels. It is better to underfeed your worm farm then overfeed. Beginners often accidentally kill their worm population because of overfeeding. They are given more food than they can process and this creates imbalances in the farm.

Trust the process. It is best to leave the worm farm alone and only open it up when feeding. It is normal to be excited and want to look in there every hour but this disturbs the worms from their work. They love the dark and privacy. Light just drives them deeper down in the farm away from food scraps. It is fine to check the bin once a week to add either bedding or moisture, but then it is best to leave it alone.

Contribute to the environment. Although it may seem like a weird hobby to some, I want to encourage you to spread the word. With worm farming you are making a positive contribution to the environment. You will discover that it is not difficult or time consuming, and it has great benefits. Be open with the fact that you have a worm farm and show people how easy it is to get started.

Worms are simultaneous hermaphrodites, meaning they have both male and female reproductive organs. It still takes two worms to reproduce.

-Josh Clark-

AFTERWORD

Roughly one third of our food ends up in the trash, globally. As a society we live very wastefully and this places tremendous pressures on landfills. How we are currently organized costs us energy, food and money. *"The United States alone spends about 165 billion dollars a year managing food wastes"

Your simple partaking in worm farming helps make a difference. Worms convert our organic waste into powerful natural fertilizers. Throughout the book we looked at how to best get started. It's a simple process that only needs a small container, some worms, bedding and some food waste.

Many enthusiasts form clubs and spread the word of worm farming, some even start businesses. As vermicompost grows in demand, the value of this "black gold" only continues to rise. Cities keep growing and with less space available we are looking for solutions in small scale farming. This all leads to vermi-composting becoming more important and helpful for our future.

Worm farming creates an asset out of our waste...

Worms are older than the dinosaurs.

-Wormfarmguru.com-

THANK YOU

Thank you for reading this book, I hope you enjoyed!

If you found the information provided useful, I would truly appreciate you leaving a review. Your honest opinion will make it easier for other readers to make a good purchasing decision. You will also be helping me compete with big publishing companies who have large advertising budgets and get hundreds of reviews. Thank you for your considerations and have an awesome day!

RESOURCES

Besides my own knowledge and experiences, I used the following awesome sources to create this book:

"11 Facts About Worms and Vermicomposting." *Nature's Little Recyclers*, nlrworms.com/blogs/education/12-facts-about-worms-and-vermicomposting.

"15 Amazing Worm Facts." *WormFarmGuru*, 29 Aug. 2018, wormfarmguru.com/amazing-worm-facts/.

Beans, Laura. "10 Interesting Facts About Earthworms." *EcoWatch*, EcoWatch, 1 Apr. 2019, www.ecowatch.-com/10-interesting-facts-about-earthworms-1881871982.html.

Chapman, Shanika. "How to Start a Worm Farm Business." *Small Business - Chron.com*, Chron.com, 26 Oct.

2016, smallbusiness.chron.com/start-worm-farm-business-39.html.

Clark, Josh. "How Earthworms Work." *HowStuffWorks*, HowStuffWorks, 16 Dec. 2011, animals.howstuffworks.-com/animal-facts/earthworm3.htm.

Clark, Josh. "How Earthworms Work." *HowStuffWorks*, HowStuffWorks, 16 Dec. 2011, animals.howstuffworks.-com/animal-facts/earthworm3.htm.

"Composting At Home." *EPA*, Environmental Protection Agency, 16 Oct. 2018, www.epa.gov/recycle/composting-home.

Conlin, Bennett. "A Step by Step Guide to Starting a Business." *Business News Daily*, 19 Mar. 2019, www.businessnewsdaily.com/4686-how-to-start-a-business.html.

Deutsche Welle. "Earthworm Numbers Dwindle, Threatening Soil Health: DW: 30.01.2017." *DW.COM*, www.dw.com/en/earthworm-numbers-dwindle-threatening-soil-health/a-37325923-0.

"Flow-Through Vermicomposting Systems." *Worm Farming Secrets*, 7 Aug. 2009, www.wormfarmingsecret-s.com/worm-beds/flow-through-vermicomposting-systems/.

"How to Harvest Worm Compost." *Worm Composting Headquarters*, www.wormcompostinghq.com/how-to-use-worm-compost/how-to-harvest-worm-compost/.

"An Introduction to Worm Farming." *Foodwise*, 26 Feb. 2014, www.foodwise.com.au/an-introduction-to-worm-farming/.

Jim, Uncle. "Harvesting Worm Castings." *Uncle Jim's Worm Farm*, 20 Sept. 2018, unclejimswormfarm.-com/harvesting-worm-castings/.

Jim, Uncle. "Random Worm Facts." *Uncle Jim's Worm Farm*, 29 Dec. 2015, unclejimswormfarm.com/random-worm-facts/.

Jim, Uncle. "Worm Composting Equipment." *Uncle Jim's Worm Farm*, 31 Dec. 2015, unclejimswormfarm.-com/worm-composting-equipment/.

"K.I.S.S. Plan for Organic Farms, Dairies, or Other Large-Scale Operations." *Worm Windrow Method for High-Volume Vermicomposting*, www.happydranch.-com/articles/Worm_Windrow_Method_For_High-Volume_Vermicomposting.htm.

McCreary, Matthew. "The Complete, 12-Step Guide to Starting a Business." *Entrepreneur*, 11 Feb. 2019, www.en-trepreneur.com/article/297899.

McDowell, C. Forrest, et al. *How to Make Compost Tea*, www.homecompostingmadeeasy.com/composttea.html.

North, Journey. *Life of an Earthworm*, jour-neynorth.org/tm/worm/WormLife.html.

TED-Ed, director. *YouTube. YouTube*, YouTube, 26 June

2013, www.youtube.com/watch?time_continue=255&v=V8miLevRI_o.

"Try Composting in Your Apartment – with a Worm Bin 🐛." *Wasteland Rebel*, wastelandrebel.com/en/apartment-composting-with-a-worm-bin/.

"What Do Worms Eat? A Helpful Guide for Feeding Worms." *WormFarmGuru*, 29 Nov. 2018, wormfarmguru.com/feeding-worms/.

"What Exactly Is Worm Farming?" *EarthChild Project*, 28 Mar. 2017, earthchildproject.org/what-exactly-is-worm-farming/.

"WORM FARMING." *Compost Collective*, compostcollective.org.nz/worm-farming/#what-to-feed-your-worms.

"WORM FARMING." *Compost Collective*, compostcollective.org.nz/worm-farming/.

Made in the USA
Columbia, SC
27 July 2022

64141754R00067